NATURAL INSTINCTS

On the ground or in the air, the LEGO® City mountain police are on the case!

The officer and the eager cadet search the mountain for a crook. "What's it like to be a mountain police officer?" asks the cadet. "There's never a dull moment!" says the officer.

"How do you spot the crooks in all this wilderness?" asks the cadet. "In the mountains, you need to trust nature and your instincts more than your eyes."

"You might see a bear,
but that's not honey in his pot!"

The officer laughs. "Another time
snakes helped me find the real snake
in the grass. High five, snakes!"

"Then there was a crook hiding behind a tree!"
"Did you catch him?" asks the cadet.

"With help from the bees!"
the officer chuckles.

"Wow, it's incredible how easily you spotted all those crooks!"
The officer smiles. "You too will soon learn how to look for clues!"

"There!" shouts the eagle-eyed officer. He sees something on the ground! "You see," says the officer, suddenly changing the direction of the flight. "The mountain is like a garden."

"You just have to learn how to spot ..."
the officer says, as he pulls a special lever.

WHOOSH!

"... the weeds!"
Suddenly, a net drops from
the helicopter!
It lands right on a tree stump.
But it's really a crook
in disguise!

"You got him!" shouts the cadet.
"Of course! When the sharp-witted mountain police
have nature on their side, no crook can outfox them!"

THE END!

NAVIGATION SKILLS

You'll start your training with the constable who will show you how to cross mountain bridges. First activity: draw the missing bridges.

START

DONUTS IN DANGER

The LEGO City police nailed some crooks at the station. Those rascals wanted to steal the entire donut supply from the police storeroom! Can you circle the 10 differences between the pictures showing the crime?

Test your skills! Help the police officer locate all the robbers rummaging through the storeroom! Write their number in the box.

DOING PAPERWORK

Police officers need to know their police vehicles very well, so they can decide which one is best for their mission. Help Chase McCain and finish the diagram of the police helicopter. Grab a pencil and get going!

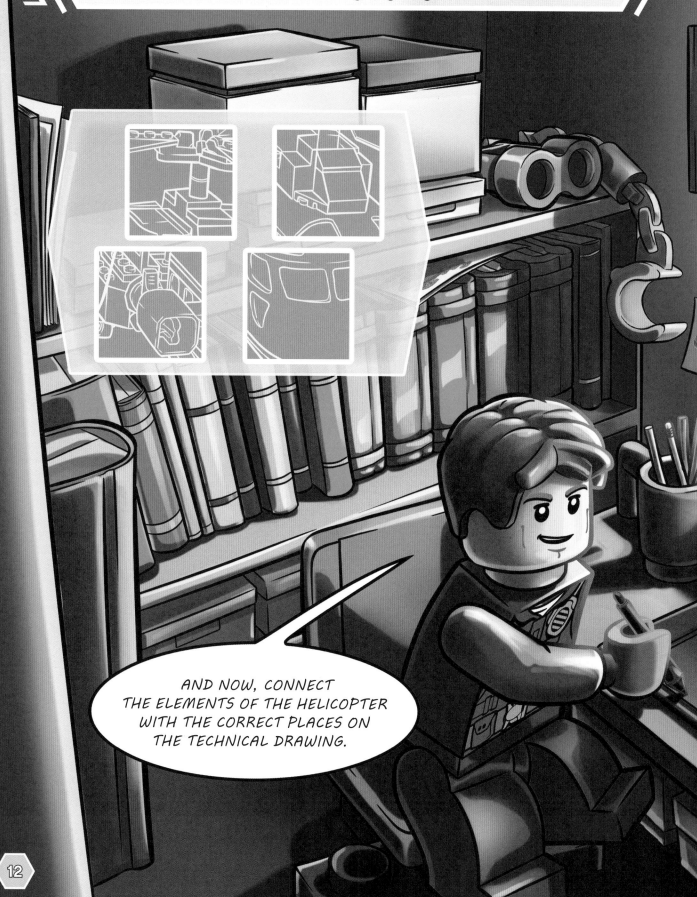

AND NOW, CONNECT THE ELEMENTS OF THE HELICOPTER WITH THE CORRECT PLACES ON THE TECHNICAL DRAWING.

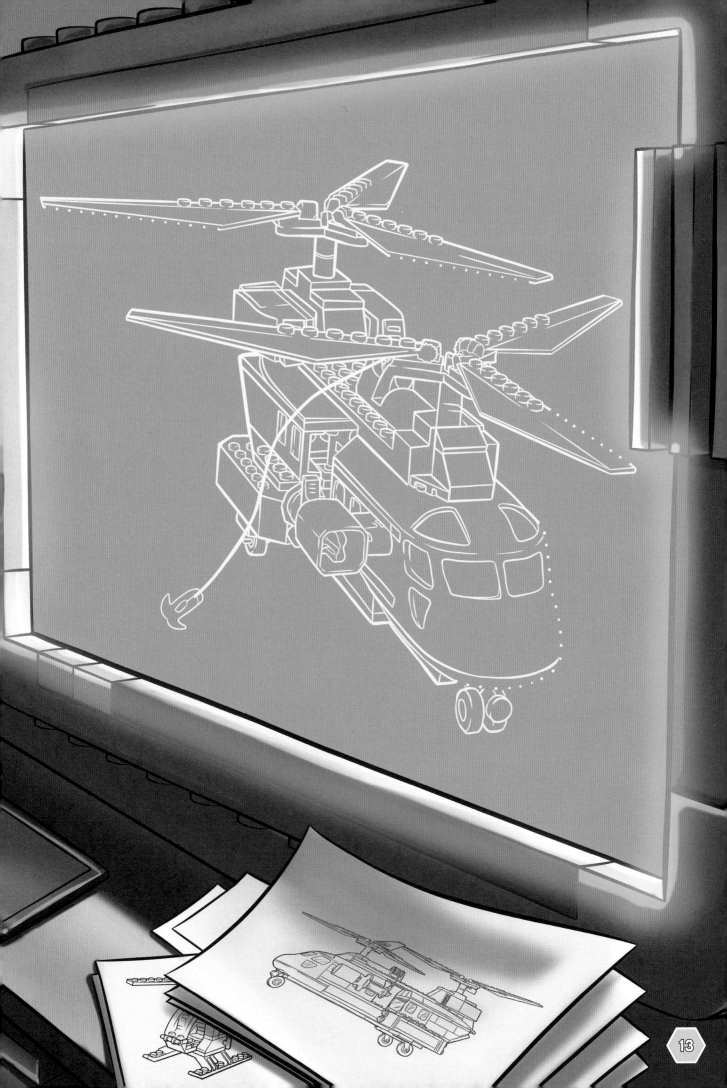

QUICK THINKING

Crooks disguised as clowns have just robbed the bank! They've thrown four different brick combinations in the air to slow down the officers. Find and count the different brick combinations, before all the bricks tumble!

BEAR SCARE!

THE END!

EQUIPMENT INSPECTION

Time for an equipment inspection! Compare a city police officer with a mountain police officer and match all the common elements in their equipment.

YOU SHOULD MANAGE TO DO IT IN THREE MINUTES, THEN WE'RE GETTING OUT INTO THE FIELD AGAIN!

FISHED OUT

As part of practising new crook-catching techniques, the mountain officers have tested an enormous net. Think you could do it too? Number the pictures from the action in the correct order.

SUSPECT STAKEOUT

In a moment, Chase McCain will test how well you can spot suspects in a stakeout. Take a look at the mugshots Chase is holding and circle the two leaders of the gang in the picture. Can you also find and circle five red crowbars?

5 x

SECURE TRANSPORT

Can you ensure the convoy of prisoners travel securely from the station in the mountains to LEGO City? Draw the route without taking your pencil off the page. Don't touch the edge! It would mean falling off the cliff!

UNDERCOVER TRAINING

The first lesson in undercover work is blending in.
Get Chase McCain ready for each assignment by drawing the
right disguise for the situation.

COLLECTING EVIDENCE

Help the police officer in this securing evidence exercise. Look at the picture and circle all the objects the arrested crook has dropped.

MOUNTAIN PATROL

Chase McCain will teach you how to patrol the difficult mountain areas. Let's see how well you handle a patrol at high altitude. Look at the infrared silhouettes to the right and mark the crooks' whereabouts in the area below.

ANSWERS

p. 8-9

p. 10-11

7

p. 12-13

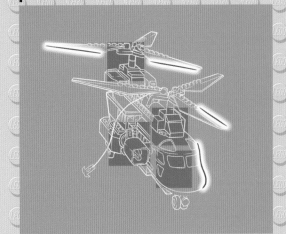

p. 14-15

p. 18

4

ANSWERS

p. 19

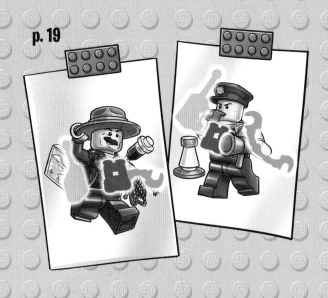

p. 20

p. 21

p. 22-23

p. 27

p. 28-29